Hidden Fur

CREATURE CAMOUFLAGE COLORING BOOK

MindWare®
brainy toys for kids of all ages®

www.mindware.com

A MindWare® Original!

Our entire selection of Brainy Toys for Kids of All Ages® is available at www.mindware.com, or by calling us at 800-999-0398 to request a catalog.

Coloring Books

Each of our coloring books offers one-of-a-kind patterns, textures and styles you make your own by choosing how to bring them to life.

Animal Habitats Series

Creature Camouflage Series

Designs Series

Illuminations Series

Lights Series

Modern Patterns Series

Mosaics Series

Quilts Series

Scapes Series

Transformations Series

Puzzle Books

Our puzzle books build skills in many areas—from logic to math, spatial reasoning to verbal skills.

Analogy Challenges

Analogy Crosswords

Clip Clue Puzzles

Code Breakers

Coin Clues

Deducibles

Directive Detective

Extreme Dot to Dot

Fast Facts Trivia

Grid Perplexors

Letter Links

Logic Links

Math Mosaics Series

Math Path Puzzles

Math Perplexors

Noodlers

Number Circuits

Number Junctions

Perplexors

Sequencers

Tactic Twisters

Tan-Tastic Tangrams

Venn Perplexors

Word Winks

Word Wise

Wordoku Puzzles

Games and Activities

Building blocks to strategic games, mystery puzzles to imaginative play — enhance abstract thinking and reasoning skills with our ingenious games and activities.

Bella's Mystery Decks

Blik-Blok

Block Buddies

Chaos

Cross-Eyed

CrossWise

Dizios

Flip 4

Gambit

Guacamole

Hue Knew?

Hue Knew? On the Go!

Loose Change

Logic Links Game

Make Your Own Mask Kit

Noodlers Game

Pattern Play

Q-bitz

Qwirkle

Qwirkle Cubes

Squzzle Puzzles

Talk In Text

Tally Rally

Up for Grabs!

Zenith

© 2004 MindWare Holdings, Inc.

Illustrations by Adam Turner
Design by Kristine Mudd

ISBN 978-1-892069-83-2
SKU 25075

for other MindWare products visit
www.mindware.com

The **White-Tailed Deer Fawn** is born with a reddish-brown coat covered with white spots. These white spots can look like flowers or filtered sunlight through the foliage, helping to camouflage the fawn while its mother is away.

The markings of a **Giraffe's** coat are unique to each animal, much like human fingerprints, and vary in color according to region. When a herd of giraffes gather, their patterns act as disruptive camouflage, confusing possible predators.

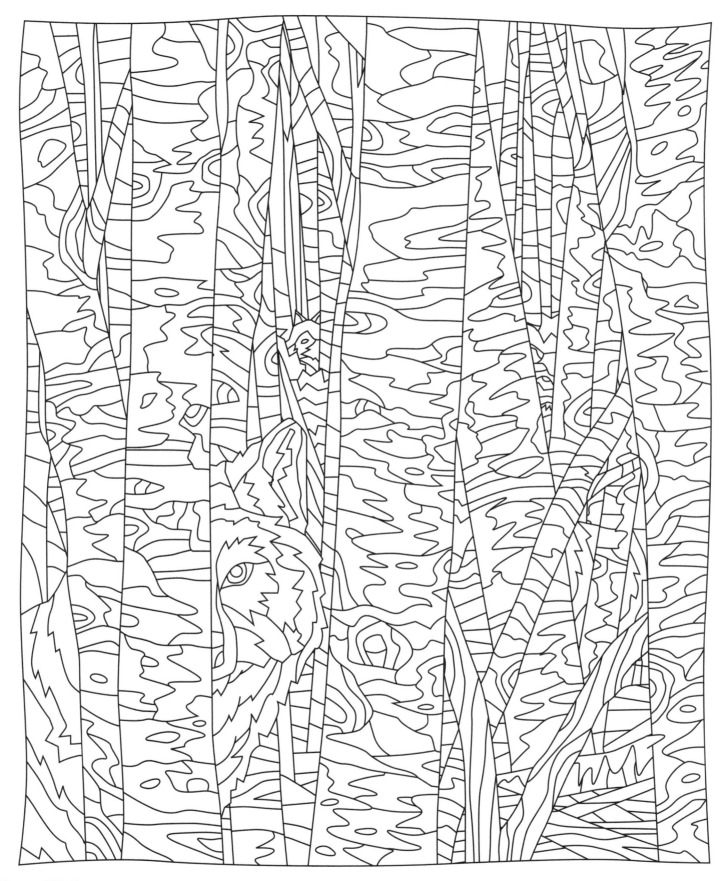

Gray Wolves often have a blend of gray, brown, black, white and even red fur. In places where the foliage changes colors throughout the year, the wolf's coat also changes colors to match the surroundings.

By wrapping its wings around its body and hanging upside down from tree limbs, the **Flying Fox Bat** exhibits superb camouflage. The bat simply looks like a large dead leaf among the dense bushes where it roosts during the day.

The olive and brown-colored coat of the **Anubis Baboon** helps to hide it in the open grasslands of the African savanna. Baboons spend their days eating grasses and roots but sleep in trees at night for extra protection.

When a **Jack Rabbit** senses danger it will freeze in position, relying on its brown coat for camouflage. If a predator starts a chase, the rabbit will run about in a zig-zag pattern and then stop suddenly, hoping to blend in with the brush.

The colorings and markings of nocturnal **Galagos**, or **Bush Babies**, allows them to become almost invisible in their environment during the day while they rest in bushes and trees, protecting themselves from predators.

Moose vary in color from very light brown to almost black. During winter months, their coats turn grayish in color, camouflaging them in the snow-covered landscape.

The muted brown and yellow coat of the **Duck-Billed Platypus** is similar to the colors found along the shores of lakes and streams and helps to camouflage the animal from its predators.

Although the **African Elephant** is a huge animal, its large gray form disappears as it stands still in the shadows of trees and thick grasses. The adult elephant has few predators, but camouflage protects young elephants from lions and tigers.

The coat of **Meadow Mice** adapts in color to the environment, allowing the mice to blend in with their surroundings. Ranging from dark black-brown to light gray-brown in color, the mice are camouflaged among foliage from hawks, owls and snakes.

The orange and black stripes of the **Bengal Tiger's** coat break up its pattern and trick prey into thinking the tiger is simply part of the environment. Hunting in the evening when shadows are long helps to further conceal this predator.

The **White-Tailed Deer Fawn** is born with a reddish-brown coat covered with white spots. These white spots can look like flowers or filtered sunlight through the foliage, helping to camouflage the fawn while its mother is away.

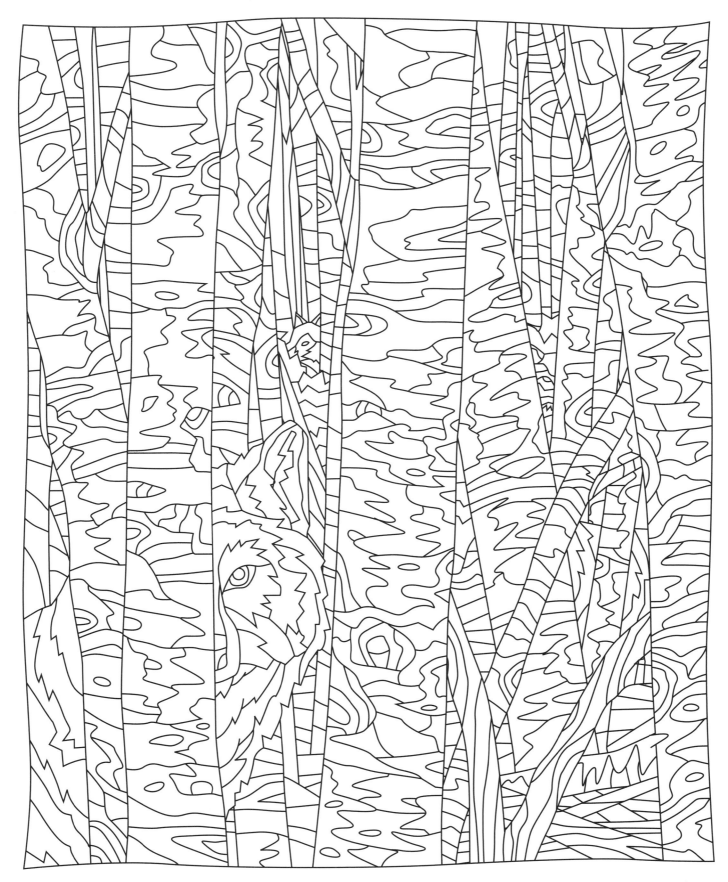

Gray Wolves often have a blend of gray, brown, black, white and even red fur. In places where the foliage changes colors throughout the year, the wolf's coat also changes colors to match the surroundings.

By wrapping its wings around its body and hanging upside down from tree limbs, the **Flying Fox Bat** exhibits superb camouflage. The bat simply looks like a large dead leaf among the dense bushes where it roosts during the day.

The olive and brown-colored coat of the **Anubis Baboon** helps to hide it in the open grasslands of the African savanna. Baboons spend their days eating grasses and roots but sleep in trees at night for extra protection.

When a **Jack Rabbit** senses danger it will freeze in position, relying on its brown coat for camouflage. If a predator starts a chase, the rabbit will run about in a zig-zag pattern and then stop suddenly, hoping to blend in with the brush.

The colorings and markings of nocturnal **Galagos**, or **Bush Babies**, allows them to become almost invisible in their environment during the day while they rest in bushes and trees, protecting themselves from predators.

Moose vary in color from very light brown to almost black. During winter months, their coats turn grayish in color, camouflaging them in the snow-covered landscape.

The muted brown and yellow coat of the **Duck-Billed Platypus** is similar to the colors found along the shores of lakes and streams and helps to camouflage the animal from its predators.

Although the **African Elephant** is a huge animal, its large gray form disappears as it stands still in the shadows of trees and thick grasses. The adult elephant has few predators, but camouflage protects young elephants from lions and tigers.

The coat of **Meadow Mice** adapts in color to the environment, allowing the mice to blend in with their surroundings. Ranging from dark black-brown to light gray-brown in color, the mice are camouflaged among foliage from hawks, owls and snakes.

The orange and black stripes of the **Bengal Tiger's** coat break up its pattern and trick prey into thinking the tiger is simply part of the environment. Hunting in the evening when shadows are long helps to further conceal this predator.